FULFILLED

Uncovering the Biblical Foundations of Catholicism

PART TWO

Drawn into the Divine Mystery

SONJA CORBITT

ASCENSION

West Chester, Pennsylvania

Nihil obstat: Reverend Stephen Gideon
              Censor deputatus

Imprimatur: + The Very Reverend J. Mark Spalding
              Bishop of Nashville
              May 30, 2018

Fulfilled: Uncovering the Biblical Foundations of Catholicism is a faith formation resource of Ascension Publishing, LLC.

Ascension
Post Office Box 1990
West Chester, PA 19380
1-800-376-0520
ascensionpress.com

Cover image: Jason Bach
Design: Rosemary Strohm

Printed in the United States of America

ISBN 978-1-945179-30-3

CONTENTS

FULFILLED

Uncovering the Biblical Foundations of Catholicism

——— PART TWO ———

Drawn into the Divine Mystery

LEADER'S NOTES

FOR STUDY LEADERS

Welcome, study leaders and small-group facilitators. I congratulate you on your willingness and obedience to God in offering this Bible study. I have prayed fervently for you!

Fulfilled is a faith-sharing crash course, a scriptural exploration of how the Old Testament Tabernacle relates to and foreshadows the Catholic Church and the individual soul.

These Leader's Notes are designed to help you facilitate a group study of *Fulfilled* in your own parish, home, or community.

Program Overview

Fulfilled: Uncovering the Biblical Foundations of Catholicism is a two-part fourteen-week Scripture study designed for individual and group work. The study set includes:

- Two workbooks *(Part One: Called into His Presence* and *Part Two: Drawn into the Divine Mystery)*, each with seven sessions

- The *Fulfilled: Uncovering the Biblical Foundations of Catholicism* book, an Amazon Best Seller which fully explores and explains the information covered in each workbook study session

- Fourteen 30-minute video presentations, one for each session in the program

Following the layout of the Old Testament Tabernacle, the program is divided into a study addressing the Outer Tabernacle *(Part One: Called into His Presence)* and a study addressing the Inner Sanctuary of the Tabernacle *(Part Two: Drawn into the Divine Mystery).* These two parts can be done in any order, but both studies require the use of the *Fulfilled* videos and book, which are necessary to run the program.

Individual Study

As a study leader of *Fulfilled: Drawn into the Divine Mystery,* you should familiarize yourself with this workbook before distributing copies to the study participants. In addition to the workbook, each participant will need his or her own copy of the *Fulfilled* book.

Each session in this workbook includes an introductory prayer, a Key Scripture verse for possible memorization, Scripture passages and questions for study, and space for personal meditation and response to God. Beginning with Session Two, participants complete the reading and questions at home prior to the group meeting. Participants should not worry if they are unable to answer every question in a session. The *Fulfilled* book will fill in the blanks, and they can bring whatever questions they still have to the small-group discussion.

Group Sessions

Participants meet once a week for 60 to 90 minutes to view a 30-minute video and to discuss their individual responses to the Scripture readings and questions in the workbook and book during the previous week.

In the video for Session One, I introduce myself and the goals and themes of the study, and I review the material covered in the Part One study as a recap for those who have done it and to help those doing Part Two first. Again, a participant can do Part Two without having already done Part One, understanding that they can do Part One the next time it is offered, and vice versa. For each of the remaining six sessions, participants watch a video of teaching that corresponds to the previous week's home preparation work. This video should be viewed before the group discussion (unless it has been assigned for at-home viewing, which is at the discretion of the leader).

After viewing the video, the study group splits into smaller groups (if necessary) to discuss the session content. Group discussions help reinforce and apply what has been learned. The small-group discussions provide accountability and a community in which participants share insights gleaned during individual study.

Leader Responsibilities

The beauty of this study format is that the only requirement to lead *Fulfilled* is a willingness to facilitate, an excitement to explore the tenets of the study, and a desire to help others share their faith and draw closer to God through Scripture. The most important elements to the success of your study will be your own commitment to Christ through the Church and doing the study work itself. After that, you will need to provide administrative leadership for the group by:

- Scheduling, promoting, and coordinating the study

- Ordering and distributing resources

- Greeting, encouraging, and communicating with participants

- Guiding (and sometimes charitably limiting) group discussion

- Facilitating prayer intentions, group prayers, and fellowship

- Arranging for simple refreshments or other forms of hospitality

- Encouraging completion of the course work

Suggested Study Schedule

No matter how you decide to schedule it, to get the most out of the study, you will want to follow this order: (1) complete the workbook session and book reading at home, (2) gather together as a group, (3) watch the session's video presentation (unless assigned for at-home viewing), and (4) discuss the session's questions in small groups.

Other Suggestions

You might want to arrange the chairs facing one another in a circle. Guide prayer intentions and sharing so that everyone who wants to participate is able to do so, but try not to push participants to respond or share more than they want to. In some groups, one participant may dominate the discussion. This person is usually a natural leader. You will want to limit this person's comments as charitably as possible, so that the entire group can be heard. Be enthusiastic, but always start and finish on time, helping the last person speaking to reach a point of conclusion if necessary. Follow up with participants individually if you discern a particular need.

Finally, remember that you are the leader. Your job is not to teach but to facilitate the sharing and discussion. Set boundaries, but be sensitive to the Holy Spirit leading his people. He has called you to this task, and he is personally involved with both you and your study group. Blessings, friend!

STUDY FORMAT

Each session of this study includes:

STEP 1: HOME PREPARATION

- *At-Home Study* – *Beginning with Session Two, you will be asked to read the workbook material before meeting, which will engage you in your faith by asking you to turn to your Catholic Bible to explore and find answers to pointed questions regarding the topics. Write your answers directly into the spaces provided in the workbook so you will be prepared to discuss them with your group. Also read the chapters in the* Fulfilled *book corresponding to each workbook session. The book offers further discussion and explanation of the covered content.*

- *Review* – *"Repetition is the mother of learning," as they say, so we spend a little time revisiting each session in a concise way.*

STEP 2: VIDEO PRESENTATION

- *Video Presentation* – *Dive deeper into each session's topic with engaging videos that present insights to further your biblical understanding of the Catholic Faith and its relationship to your life.*

STEP 3: SMALL-GROUP DISCUSSION

- *An Invitation* – *This section applies Scripture and the session's insights to your life and helps facilitate small-group discussion. This is when you can discuss your answers during Home Preparation.*

- *A God Prompt* – *Here, I offer a LOVE the Word™ exercise,* lectio divina *without the Latin, to practice getting in touch with God directly and personally. These prompts can help facilitate further group discussion, while others invite you to reflect personally on a topic's connection to your life.*

Introduction

Our Father, who art in heaven, hallowed be thy name;
thy kingdom come, thy will be done,
on earth as it is in heaven. Amen.

As a non-Catholic, I was known as a "soul-winning," faith-sharing fiend among the pastors in our association of churches. My denomination hosted a toy store missionary outreach every Christmas, in which community members in financial straits could shop for their families for free.

Hundreds of volunteers assembled at the First Denominational Church in our town. Classrooms on a long hall of one wing of the education building teemed with toys, clothes, and household items. At the opposite hall, a row of smaller classrooms formed the bar of the "T," in which religious counseling was offered for the guests who consented. Since there was no exit from the building except at that end, we counselors stationed ourselves there as "angels" who helped guests to their cars with their gifts.

I was both the rare female and only faith counselor under the age of thirty. Every annual group of pastors serving as counselors commended my effectiveness and missionary zeal.

God was certainly going to use me mightily in his kingdom, they would say, nodding to one another and to me, as I barely waited to spring the trap of my idealism on the guests coming down the hall. I especially relished "picking off" the Catholics, and the other counselors often reserved them for me.

"Are you saved?" I would ask with a bright smile to mitigate the confrontation. "Have you asked Jesus into your heart? Will you go to heaven when you die? How do you know? Don't you want to know where you will spend eternity? I can tell you how to know for sure. Here, let me show you in the Bible."

And because I could show them chapter and verse as I led them through a concise faith-sharing model, I led many a blind Catholic away from the Church.

TO EQUIP THE SAINTS FOR THE WORK OF MINISTRY (EPHESIANS 4:12)

Now, my head and heart and faith are fulfilled in the Catholic Church. Thinking back on the blank stares of the Catholics I used to question—and their inability to concisely answer my zealous presumption—is what motivates my entire ministry today. I see with painful regularity how quickly God's "people are destroyed for lack of knowledge" (Hosea 4:6), even as they yearn to share the beautiful practices that animate their lives with those they know and love.

I know you long to be able to explain this glorious, ever-ancient, ever-new Catholic Faith in a way that will not only intrigue, but also inspire others to investigate and embrace the Church more fully. That's why you are here.

Because I was once an adversary, by God's relentless mercy I know how to answer this longing. I languish *with* you.

When an understanding of the Catholic Faith clicked for me through the divine biblical model I am sharing with you in *Fulfilled*, I spent the long, dark hours of an entire night on my face before the Lord, sobbing with remorse over my denominational ignorance and error, begging him to give me the opportunity to win back the Catholics I stole away and to make me an instrument of unity in the Church.

DISCOVERING THE BIBLICAL FOUNDATIONS OF CATHOLICISM

Those of you who have participated in Part One of *Fulfilled* have been introduced to this faith-sharing model. For everyone else, know that in the previous six sessions in Part One, we began exploring the Old Testament Tabernacle as the biblical foundation for the Catholic Faith. A recap of Part One follows.

We looked at the outer sanctuary of the Tabernacle, comparing how Jesus gave the Old Testament—the formal, physical Tabernacle; liturgical schedule; institutional priesthood; blood sacrifice on the bronze altar; perpetual altar fire; and ritual washings—new life.

Just as Jesus' death, resurrection, and ascension into heaven were not the end, but the beginning of the Church; just as Jesus' physical body was "fulfilled" and yet remains; the Old Testament was fulfilled and yet remains in his mystical body, the Church.

The blueprint of the Old Testament remains the template of the New Testament. Like Jesus' almost unrecognizable resurrected body (see John 20:14), the old practices and prescriptions, in him, are dead and resurrected, changed and filled with supernatural saving grace.

Through the Church, Jesus would not just tabernacle among men, as in the Old Testament and the tabernacle of his own body,

St Ambrose barring Theodosius from Milan Cathedral by Anthony van Dyck (c. 1619–1620)

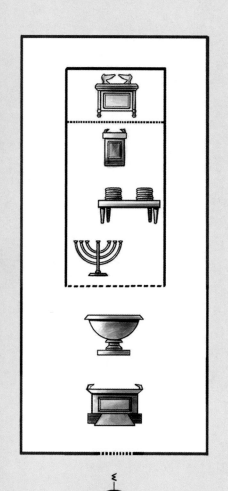

but tabernacle *in* men, through his body the Church, itself a living tabernacle (see 1 Peter 2:5).

Remember that the Old Testament Tabernacle was prescribed by God himself in order to instruct his people in proper worship. The Tabernacle foreshadowed worship in the Church *and* in heaven. The Tabernacle was meant to be the structural basis of all Christian worship and practice. Both Old Testament and New Testament worship are modeled after the worship occurring in heaven right now, as seen in the prophetic books, and reflected in the individual soul.

Catholic rituals and practices may sometimes seem old fashioned, outdated, or even unbiblical, but they are all rooted in the Old Testament Tabernacle. Isn't it comforting to know there are specific reasons for all we do in Catholic worship?

THE TABERNACLE

A portable tent-like structure and a surrounding external courtyard, the strictly prescribed Tabernacle setup informed the Israelites that they could only come to God in the way he offered. There was no other way. As we have seen, God used the Old Testament Tabernacle to tell us that we, too, can only come to him most fully through the way he has provided for us—the historical Church in Jesus Christ.

The shape of the layout is the Cross of Christ. The Church imitates this cruciform shape and proportions in its individual churches. Jesus said he did not come to cancel the Old Testament, but to give us the grace to keep it more perfectly than in just our outward behavior, so that we ourselves also fulfill the Law, in him (see Matthew 5:17-19, 9:16-17).

Jesus came to build something gloriously new on the foundation of the old structure. As the new Tabernacle, he imbues the New Covenant with a new spirit. He teaches us its proper orientation and meaning and gives it all saving power. The Old Covenant is not canceled, as in tossed out as "wrong" or "bad," he says, even in its minutiae. In fact, Jesus offers his gravest warning to anyone who would simply relax, much less eradicate, even one detail.

Jesus gathers in, upholds, and expands the entire Old Testament, in every detail, into and beyond himself. In his Person, even until the end of heaven and earth, he brings it forward and fills it with a breath and grace that makes the new structure alive, and therefore capable of salvation.

Let's review all the important elements of the outer sanctuary and how they apply to us in the Church.

PART ONE: THE OUTER SANCTUARY

First and foremost, the Church is the final, eternal tabernacle of God as Christ's mystical body (see Revelation 21:3). In the Old Testament, there were times when God withdrew his Spirit from the Tabernacle or from the Temple because of the people's sins. But after Jesus' perfect sacrifice, that can never happen again. Because the Church is the "house" or tabernacle in the New Testament, as St. Paul says, it is therefore the foundation of truth (see 1 Timothy 3:15).

Because the Church is made of individual Christians, you, too, are a living tabernacle of God. For God to feel completely at home and dwell most fully in us, every worship element of the Old Testament Tabernacle should be reflected in our own lives. The fullness of the Faith has been preserved in the Catholic Church so that each prescribed element is present in the faithful Catholic's life today.

LITURGICAL YEAR

Observing the liturgical worship schedule of the Church is a happy privilege. Through our liturgical year, we "keep time" with God and all the saints and angels of history, present, and future. As in the Old Testament, our special days include rest, offerings, and a sacred assembly.

Holy days and feast days are special because they remind us of important salvation events in our history with God. Jesus fulfilled the Old Testament feasts, so our holy days revolve around him and his life and ministry—Sunday, Christmas, and Easter—and those saints who served him most extravagantly. St. Paul tells us plainly to "celebrate the festival [feast]" (1 Corinthians 5:7-8). Every Catholic holy and feast day is centered on the New Covenant himself, in the Eucharist.

PRIESTHOOD

As the Old Testament and Ezekiel's prophetic messianic temple prescribe, there is both a ministerial and lay priesthood in the Catholic Church. "And like living stones be yourselves built into a spiritual house, to be a holy priesthood, to offer spiritual sacrifices acceptable to God through Jesus Christ" (1 Peter 2:5).

The Old Testament liturgical year foreshadows the Catholic liturgical year.

Our Catholic priesthood serves God's people through the new sacramental economy founded on Christ in the Eucharist. Every Christian is also called to a form of priesthood. We lay "priests" can offer all of our sacrifices in union with Christ for the good of souls. Because Jesus appoints his priests and rules through our Catholic priesthood, to obey the legitimate authority of our priests is to obey Christ (see Romans 13:1-2).

THE BRONZE ALTAR

The bronze altar in the Tabernacle was the location for all the bloody, burnt offerings. Jesus is both the High Priest and Victim. He is the ultimate Sacrifice; the perfect Lamb of God who takes away the sin of the world. The Cross is his altar and ours, too. The sacrificial system is transformed in Jesus, and in us as his mystical body, who follows him in all things.

Following in the sacrificial footsteps of Christ, we can offer up our own sufferings as a sacrifice to God for our good and the good of souls. Remember, Eucharist means thanksgiving. We give thanks for the ultimate Sacrifice by taking up the chalice of salvation and calling on the name of the Lord (see Psalm 116:12-13).

ALTAR FIRE

Throughout Scripture, God revealed his all-consuming love for his people through fire, "for our God *is* a consuming fire" (Hebrews 12:29, emphasis added). What a thrilling thought.

"Set me as a seal upon your heart, as a seal upon your arm; for love is strong as death, jealousy is cruel as the grave. Its flashes are flashes of fire, a most vehement flame" (Song of Solomon 8:6).

The "fiery trials" and sufferings we experience in our lives are ultimately the presence of God accepting our many daily offerings throughout the primary offering of our whole life: heart, soul, mind, and strength. This fiery presence purifies us with the strength of his love, and so he is the cleansing fire associated with purgatory. God, himself, is the fire that purifies and saves us (see 1 Corinthians 3:12-15).

BRONZE LAVER

All of Christendom agrees that the Old Testament laver foreshadowed ritual baptism. Baptism configures the soul for grace and initiates us into the life of Christ. "Jesus answered, 'Truly, truly, I say to you, unless

The levitical priesthood is **fulfilled** in the Catholic priesthood.

The bronze altar is **fulfilled** in the Catholic sacrificial altar.

The Tabernacle altar fire is **fulfilled** in purgatory.

one is born of water and the spirit, he cannot enter the kingdom of God'" (John 3:5). Confession keeps the soul clean: "If we confess our sins, he is faithful and just, and will forgive our sins and cleanse us from all unrighteousness" (1 John 1:9).

PART TWO: THE INNER SANCTUARY

In Part Two of *Fulfilled,* we will explore the remaining facilities of the inner sanctuary of the Old Testament Tabernacle: the lampstand, the Table of Presence Bread, the incense altar, the veil, and the Ark of the Covenant. Through this divine model, we will come to appreciate two thousand years of biblical Church teaching on the Scriptures and Magisterium; Eucharist; prayer; and Mary. Finally, we will practice applying the Old Testament Tabernacle as *the* faith-sharing model of biblical Catholicism.

There are special features at the end of each session to help you connect your faith and the practice of it with the Old Testament and New Testament. These include:

- A **Review:** Since "repetition is the mother of learning," we briefly revisit the main points of each session.

- An **Invitation,** which applies the Scripture passages and the themes presented in the session to your life. *Note: This book quotes from the Revised Standard Version – Catholic Edition (RSV–CE) of the Bible.*

- A **God Prompt – LOVE the Word™** exercise that will help you practice getting in touch with God directly and personally.

Part Two of *Fulfilled* will finish arming you with a new apologetics resource and teach you how to answer false—or at least incomplete—interpretations of Scripture with the fullness of Catholic history and teaching. It is my hope that you will no longer be intimidated by a lack of information and will be equipped with a clear, convenient way to communicate the truths of the Faith in light of Scripture.

YOU ARE NOW READY FOR THE **SESSION ONE VIDEO.**

The Tabernacle laver is *fulfilled* in confession and baptism.

VIDEO PRESENTATION

Session One: Introduction

Review of Part One: The Outer Sanctuary

- Genres and typology are important in the Bible.

- God wants to be close to us.

- Old Testament liturgical calendar; Church's liturgical calendar

- Old Testament priest; Jesus as High Priest; Catholic priest

- Bronze altar prefigures Catholic altar

- Fire prefigures purgatory

- Laver prefigures baptismal font

Introduction to Part Two: The Inner Sanctuary

- Lampstand prefigures Magisterium

- Table of Presence Bread prefigures Eucharist

- Incense altar prefigures Catholic prayer

- Veil conceals God

- Ark of the Covenant prefigures Mary as new tabernacle

SMALL-GROUP DISCUSSION

Because there is no home preparation to review in this introductory session, spend time getting to know the members in your group. Allow ten to fifteen minutes to go around the room and let each member spend two to three minutes introducing themselves.

Spend the remaining time in your small group answering these questions:

1. Why are you here?

2. If you participated in Part One, what was the most significant thing you learned about the Catholic Faith in that study? What was the most significant thing you learned about yourself?

3. What do you hope to get out of this study?

The Light of Truth

May the light of God surround us, the love of God enfold us,
the power of God protect us, the presence of God watch over us.
Wherever we are, God is, and where God is, all is well. Amen.

STEP 1:
HOME PREPARATION

So far, our exploration of the Old Testament Tabernacle has only involved the outer court. In Part One of *Fulfilled,* we compared how Jesus' sacrifice on the Cross satisfied the Old Testament requirement for blood sacrifice on the bronze altar. But that was not the end. Jesus rose from the dead! Alleluia! He came back, not just to tabernacle among men, as God did in the Old Testament and as Jesus did in the tabernacle of his own body, but to tabernacle *in* men.

After exploring the sacrifices of the altar, we proceeded to the cleansing, sacramental waters of his baptism. In the outer court of the Tabernacle, everything was about blood, judgment, death, cleansing, and purification. But now, we enter the inner court, the sanctuary and Holy Place, where everything is about life, food, light, and the fragrance of incense. It is quiet, silent even.

TABERNACLE LIGHT

In the Old Testament Tabernacle, a copy of the temple in heaven, the sanctuary was covered with curtains. To the left of the sanctuary entrance was a piece of equipment used to illuminate it. According to **Exodus 25:31-40,** what was this instrument?

According to the pattern God gave Moses on Mount Sinai, the base, shaft, branches, bowls, ornamental knobs, and flowers of this instrument were hammered from one gold piece (see **Exodus 25:31**). Like a tree of gold, the lampstand was the article on which the most adornment was lavished. The sanctuary would have been aglow in its light, flickering against the gold on the walls.

2 ▸ What do you think is the significance of the "one gold piece"?

3 ▸ Compare this idea with **John 15:5.**

4 ▸ With what fascinating floral detail should the Tabernacle menorah be decorated?

5 ▸ Do you remember from Part One what the almond branch is symbolic of? (See back for answer if you have not yet participated in Part One.)

6 ▸ Turn to **Revelation 1:12-20.** We thoroughly covered the priesthood and the biblical numerology of seven. Can you discern what is happening here? Explain. (See back for answer if you have not yet participated in Part One.)

7 The responsibilities regarding the lampstand are given in **Exodus 27:20-21** and **Leviticus 24:1-4,** through which we gather interesting details about priestly ministry. Jot the requirements down here.

The nature of the light-bearing priesthood becomes clear through an investigation of the scriptural uses and Hebrew view of "light."

8 Please turn to **Exodus 28:29-30.** This section is a description of two particular parts of the priestly vestments that we have not yet encountered. The "breastplate of judgment" was a pocket of sorts, sewn together on three sides and open at the top. What was in the special pocket?

These titles are transliterated, meaning the Hebrew characters are simply changed to corresponding English letters. This is usually done when there is nothing in English to correspond to an ancient word or idea.

These transliterated Hebrew words mean "Lights" and "Perfect Truths" (or the "revelation of perfect knowledge"), and both are used in the superlative plural. (See also Sirach 45:10.) Together the names mean something similar to "Perfect Knowledge."

9 In the following passages, please indicate how and why the stones were used:

Numbers 27:21 –

1 Samuel 14:41 –

Ezra 2:63 –

Decalogue Parchment by Jekuthiel Sofer (c. 1768)

10 It is thought that the priest would somehow cast lots to determine the will of God in a matter. What does **Sirach 45:10** call the Urim and Thummim?

Exactly what the stones looked like or how they were used is unknown, but apparently, the high priest phrased direct questions to God in the Holy of Holies so that they could be answered with a simple "yes" or "no," signified by the withdrawing of the corresponding stones from the priest's pocket or ephod. This is why the Urim and Thummim were stored in the breastplate of judgment.

Because of the use of the Urim and Thummim to communicate God's Word and will, the Church Fathers understood the "Lights and Truths" to mean the light of doctrine.

Similarly, part of the duty of the priesthood was to instruct and teach the people about the Law (see **Deuteronomy 33:8-10**) so that between the Ten Commandments, the Torah, and the Urim and Thummim, the people would have comprehensive judgments and teachings they could trust, teachings the Scriptures repeatedly call "light." In fact, institutional priesthood throughout the Old Testament and Jewish thought was synonymous with doctrine and teaching.

MORE OLD TESTAMENT LIGHT

11 Read through the following Scripture verses. In the space provided, indicate the main event or association the Jews had with "light," paying close attention to the development of the idea:

Genesis 1:1-5 –

Exodus 10:21-23 –

What the Church says

"*There is an organic connection between our spiritual life and the dogmas. Dogmas are lights along the path of faith; they illuminate it and make it secure. Conversely, if our life is upright, our intellect and heart will be open to welcome the light shed by the dogmas of faith.*"

— **CCC 89**

Exodus 13:17-22 –

Psalm 27:1 –

Isaiah 60:19 –

Job 29:3 –

Micah 7:8 –

Israel's preservation from the plague of darkness prefigured the light of God in the Tabernacle.

12 Over and over in biblical symbolism, light equaled deliverance from darkness. Perhaps because of repeated, miraculous deliverances, the Jewish rabbis came to refer to the coming Messiah as *Nehira*, "the Light." Taken altogether, the verses above illustrate that light was a metaphor in Old Testament Judaism for what?

JESUS AS LIGHT OF THE WORLD

13 Please turn to **John 8** and read through the chapter. The heart of this passage is found in an "I AM" metaphor that John uses seven times in different ways to present Jesus to us in his Gospel. In **verse 12,** Jesus makes the second "I AM" statement of this Gospel. What does he say he is?

14 Discerning from the context of the chapter, what kind of light does he mean?

15 If you turn back a bit to **John 7:2,** you see Jesus probably made this declaration in the context of one of the great Jewish religious festivals commanded by God, the Feast of Tabernacles. Jot down what you remember about this feast from Part One. (See back for answer if you have not yet participated in Part One.)

16 The first evening of the festival was called the "Illumination of the Temple," as four great lampstands were set ablaze in the Temple. What do you think these enormous menorahs symbolized at the feast?

17 What claim, then, would the Jewish leaders have understood Jesus to be making when he said, "I am the light of the world," at the Feast of Tabernacles?

LIGHT IN THE CHURCH

18 According to St. Paul, in **2 Thessalonians 2:15** and **3:6,** what two pillars make up authentic apostolic teaching?

19 Can the Bible ever be a Christian's only authority, then? Explain.

What the Church says

" The Magisterium is not superior to the Word of God, but is its servant. It teaches only what has been handed on to it. At the divine command and with the help of the Holy Spirit, it listens to this devotedly, guards it with dedication and expounds it faithfully. All that it proposes for belief as being divinely revealed is drawn from this single deposit of faith. "

— **CCC 86**

20 Look up the following Scripture passages and jot a summary for each:

2 Peter 1:20 –

Revelation 19:10 –

John 5:39-40 –

21 Comparing these passages together, what part of Scripture is a matter of private interpretation?

22 If authoritative interpretation of Scripture is not a private matter, it must be public. If it is public, where must we find authoritative, reliable interpretation, according to St. Paul in **1 Timothy 3:15?**

"The Church, the 'pillar and bulwark of the truth,' 'has received this solemn command of Christ from the apostles to announce the saving truth.'[1] 'To the Church belongs the right always and everywhere to announce moral principles, including those pertaining to the social order, and to make judgments on any human affairs to the extent that they are required by the fundamental rights of the human person or the salvation of souls'" (*Catechism of the Catholic Church* (CCC) 2032).

---

[1] CIC, can. 747 2.

[2] 1 Tim 3:15; LG 17.

LET'S REVIEW

The Catholic Magisterium has the authority and duty to teach and guard the Word of God and all that is worthy of belief because:

- Throughout the Old Testament, God communicated that authoritative light comes from his presence and his Word through the priesthood.

- The golden menorah was the only light source in the sanctuary.

- The decorative almond blossoms and branches on the Tabernacle lampstand were symbolic of the institutional priesthood in God's presence.

- Jesus is the Word of God, depicted in the heavenly temple as present at the center of the priesthood throughout Church history.

- Even when the priesthood is marred by faithlessness, God is faithful, for he cannot deny himself (see 2 Timothy 2:13).

- Scripture shows us that, through Christ, the magisterial priesthood interprets Scripture and speaks on faith and morals with God's authority.

- The Catholic Church is the only church on earth with both an apostolic and magisterial priesthood.

- For more on this topic, read "The Light of Truth: The Lampstand Is Fulfilled in the Magisterium" in Part Two of *Fulfilled: Uncovering the Biblical Foundations of Catholicism,* the trade book that accompanies the *Fulfilled* study.

YOU ARE NOW READY FOR THE **SESSION TWO VIDEO.**

STEP 2:
VIDEO PRESENTATION

Session Two: The Light of Truth

- Chair of the Rock, Papacy, and Magisterium as the Light of Christ

- Chair of Moses (Exodus 18:13-27)

- Early Sanhedrin (Numbers 11:16-17)

- Jesus said to obey the kathedra, chair (Matthew 23:2)

- Judgment seat of Christ (2 Corinthians 5:10)

- Jewish priesthood (Isaiah 22:16; Matthew 23:27)

- Prophecy of "office" of new steward, new keys (Isaiah 22:15-25)

- Peter as rock of the Church (Matthew 16:17-19)

Moses by Michelangelo Buonarroti, Tomb (1505–1545) for Julius II,
San Pietro in Vincoli (Rome)

STEP 3:
SMALL-GROUP DISCUSSION

INVITATION

In Jewish thought and in the Old and New Testaments, God's Word is synonymous with his presence, his light, and his priesthood. Therefore, it is God's presence in his Word, through his priesthood, that brings light. The individual Christian's responsibility to read and study the Bible for himself must take place under the Magisterium of the Church if the Bible is to be learned and practiced without error. Just as the seven lampstands surrounding Jesus in the heavenly temple (see Revelation 1:12-13) depict Jesus at the center of the institutional, Catholic priesthood, the same seven lampstands radiating outwardly from the Light of the World depict the whole of the historical Church, led by the episcopacy, as the sacred illumination of the world.

Notes

_____

_____

_____

_____

_____

_____

_____

_____

_____

_____

_____

_____

GOD PROMPT — LOVE THE WORD™

LISTEN: "Obey your leaders and submit to them; for they are keeping watch over your souls, as men who will have to give account" (Hebrews 13:17).

OBSERVE: Pray and ask God to identify one or more statements or passages from Scripture from this chapter that he wants you to understand, memorize, or practice. Perhaps you would like to underline it (or them).

In your life and circumstances, where do you need more light from God?

Do you want him to order and bring purpose to your circumstances? Do you want his light?

What will this require of you?

VERBALIZE: Lord, the most meaningful statement or Bible passage through which you spoke to me in this chapter was ...

Lord, I believe that in response to my reading in this chapter, you want me to ...

As I think about my problem, challenge, or circumstance, I need your light here ...

When I think about what your light might reveal to me about my circumstances, I feel ...

I need your help to ...

ENTRUST: *Lord, I believe. Help my unbelief! Amen.*

The Bread of Life

God is great, God is good, let us thank him for our food.
By his hands we all are fed. Give us, Lord, our daily bread. Amen.

STEP 1: HOME PREPARATION

Nothing is better than fresh-baked bread still warm from the oven and slathered with enough butter to make it swim. For me, it is one of life's simple pleasures, but more than that, bread is the stuff of life, the basis of nourishment for every people. Because it was such a basic staple, God included it in the Tabernacle to show how it could also be the basis of nourishment in the spiritual life.

Before the Tabernacle bread, however, God taught the Israelites the significance of bread in several other important ways.

OLD TESTAMENT BREAD

Melchizedek Offers Bread and Wine

One way to determine how Scripture intends a word, idea, or element like bread to be understood is by looking at the first biblical occurrence. The first offering of bread and wine to God occurs in **Genesis 14:18-20.**

1 Please read through the verses and record anything you think is noteworthy.

This is the only description in the Bible of the actual person Melchizedek. His biblical entrance and exit both occur in these three verses. He just seems to appear in the middle of a conflict between Abram and another king.

But many other biblical authors place enormous importance on Melchizedek. We also hear his name in the Church's first Eucharistic Prayer of the Mass: "Be pleased to look upon these offerings ... and to accept them, as once you were pleased to accept the ... offering of your high priest Melchizedek." We will see why in a few moments.

KEY SCRIPTURE

"I am the living bread which came down from heaven; if anyone eats of this bread, he will live forever."

— **John 6:51**

Passover Bread

In **Exodus 12,** we find another description of one of the earliest offerings of bread to communicate a significant message. Please turn there and read through the chapter, scanning for answers to the following questions. (See also **Numbers 11:8.**)

2 ▸ What was this great event in Israelite history?

3 ▸ Do you remember why Passover was important to the Israelites?

4 ▸ How was bread significant in this annual observance?

5 ▸ What were the instructions regarding the bread?

6 ▸ Can you remember from Part One why the bread had to be unleavened? (See **Exodus 12:39.**)

7 ▸ Read **Exodus 13:3-10.** What, if any, new information do you gather from these verses?

Manna

A little more than a month after the Israelites were rescued from Egypt that first Passover, they began to run out of food in the desert, where food and water were scarce. In their weariness and probably in their worry, they complained against God. Turn to **Exodus 16** and read through the chapter.

"What is it?" the Israelites asked, when it appeared on the wilderness floor, and so they named it "manna," meaning "what?" Read through **Exodus 16:14-31,** scanning for answers to the following questions:

The People Gather Manna From Heaven
by Alexander Ivanov (19th century)

8 What was the manna?

9 When did it appear?

10 What did it look and taste like?

11 How many ways were the people able to use it?

12 For how long did the miraculous manna appear for the Israelites every morning (**verse 35**)?

13 What, then, can you conclude about how nutritionally balanced and complete the manna must have been?

14 What were God's instructions and prohibitions regarding the manna? (See also **Numbers 11:8.**)

15 Why do you think the people were instructed this way?

16 Turn to **Wisdom 16:20-21.** What thoughtful provision did God include in the sustenance he supplied?

The manna showed God's sweetness to the people.

Covenant Bread

17 Read through **Exodus 24.** Do you find it interesting that when Israel ratified the covenant with God at the foot of Mount Sinai, they "ate and drank" a covenant meal? This meal likely included meat from the burnt offerings and bread and wine to make a grand celebration of the presence of God. What are your thoughts about this?

Tabernacle Bread

Directly across from the golden lampstand in the Tabernacle sanctuary, outside the Holy of Holies, was a crowned, gold table set to the right. The description of the table is in **Exodus 25:23-30.**

18 What was this table used for according to **verse 30?**

The name of this bread is remarkable. In Hebrew, it literally means "Bread of the Face [of God]," or "Bread of the Presence." Because it was located in the Tabernacle, where God's presence dwelt, it was bread where God was present and was placed perpetually *in* his presence. Even when the people moved through the wilderness, this bread was to remain on the gold table (**Numbers 4:5-7**).

19 Turn to **Leviticus 24:5-9** and jot down the highlights about this table and bread.

20 Do you remember the significance of the number of loaves? (See back for answer if you have not yet participated in Part One.)

Presence Bread was a reminder of God's perpetual provision, and it was a communal offering rather than a sacrificial one. The people actually baked the loaves, but because the bread was especially connected to God's presence, it was holy bread. It was to be eaten by the priests every Sabbath "in a holy place," the sanctuary, as they replaced the previous week's bread with fresh bread each week. Along with the bread, there were also offerings of incense, wine, and oil.

What the Church says

" *There is more hunger for love and appreciation in this world than for bread.* "

— **St. Teresa of Calcutta (Mother Teresa)**

21 God did not eat the bread, so why do you suppose it was such an integral part of the sanctuary in the Tabernacle?

22 How long was this observance to last (**Leviticus 24:5-9**)?

Each of these was to be an eternal observance. The offering of Melchizedek would be messianic; Passover was a perpetual annual feast; a memorial pot of manna was included in the Ark within the Holy of Holies; the covenant God made with his people was everlasting; and the Presence Bread was a perpetual staple in the Tabernacle.

The Presence Bread, offering of Melchizedek, Passover bread, and manna all conveyed a single theme: God was with his people in the most basic, nourishing stuff of life—bread. He was ever-present, feeding and providing for them with care and love. But there was another important reason he miraculously furnished it.

NEW TESTAMENT BREAD

Jesus, a Better Melchizedek

These provisions of bread were types of another bread to come. The new offering and new bread is the antitype, or the thing foreshadowed by the type. Recall that an antitype is always greater than a type. The term "Presence Bread" as Old Testament type foreshadows Jesus' actual, supernatural presence in the New Testament fulfillment of the Eucharist.

23 Please read **Hebrews 5:5-6,** in which Psalm 110:4 is quoted. Of whom does it speak?

Since the New Testament applies Psalm 110:4 to Jesus, we understand that Melchizedek was a type of Jesus—both somehow priests forever, kings of peace, without origin, offering bread and wine!

What the *Church* says

" The other sacraments, and indeed all ecclesiastical ministries and works of the apostolate, are bound up with the Eucharist and are oriented toward it. The Most Blessed Eucharist contains the entire spiritual boon of the Church,(16) that is, Christ himself, our Pasch and Living Bread. "

— ***Pope Paul VI,***
Presbyterorum Ordinis

Jesus, the New Moses

24 What is the event recorded in **Luke 9:28-36?**

25 What were Moses, Elijah, and Jesus talking about in **verse 31?**

26 Of the six translations I consulted, only one translated this word as "exodus," but that is its literal meaning. What, if any, significance does the word exodus have in this context, in your opinion?

27 Please turn to **John 6,** in which Jesus offers his most personal teachings on the coming Eucharist. Take a look at the chapter and paragraph headings in bold print, and list them here.

Notice what Jesus does first in this chapter: He illustrates how he can multiply bits of bread to feed thousands of people. Right after that, he proves, again, that he is Lord of natural elements by walking on the sea.

Jesus, the New Manna

Now read **verses 26-71.** Once Jesus knows the people understand that he is a prophet, he compares himself to Moses, the greatest prophet in the history of God's people. *Then,* he makes one of the boldest statements of his entire ministry. Jesus' teaching here must be understood in the context of the Old Testament bread, as he pointed out.

28▸ What does Jesus say about himself in **John 6:35?**

29▸ What does he mean?

30▸ Once they understood how literally Jesus was speaking, what did many disciples do in **John 6:66?**

In John 6, we learn Jesus is our new Melchizedek, our new Moses, our new Manna, and our new Presence Bread. Rather than mere bread and wine to nourish natural life, Jesus offers the Eucharistic Bread of his Body and wine of his Blood for eternal life. He is our new Moses, who leads and feeds us with the Bread of Life on our exodus to the Promised Land of heaven. He is the true Presence Bread, the Bread of the Face of God, of whom we are instructed to literally eat, the sustenance of the soul.

PRESENCE BREAD IN THE CHURCH

Daily Bread

31▸ Turn to **Matthew 6:9-13.** What is this familiar prayer called?

32▸ Notice, especially, **verse 11:** "Give us this day our daily bread." I always wondered why Jesus was redundant here, using "this day" and "daily" in the same sentence. What are your own thoughts about this repetition?

Fresco by Wolfgang Andreas Heindl
(c. 1722–1724)

33 Please read **John 6:63** and write a sentence of synopsis in the space below.

"Spiritual" never means symbolic; it means super- or hyper-natural. "Spiritual" bread means more-than-just-bread. Moses' daily manna fed the natural lives of God's people, but the Bread of Life, Jesus, feeds us supernatural, eternal life daily.

Eucharistic Bread

Because eternal life is in him, Jesus commanded us to eat his flesh and drink his blood. The Church did not invent the Eucharist; it received it from Jesus on the night before his crucifixion and continues to offer it to this day at his command.

Eucharist means thanksgiving. At the annual Passover meal, Jesus took bread, gave thanks and broke it, and gave it to the disciples saying, "This is my body which is given for you. Do this in remembrance of me" (Luke 22:19).

34 Do you think the twelve disciples could have doubted what Jesus was referring to, given their familiarity with the twelve loaves of Presence Bread provided daily in the Temple, Moses' manna, and their annual Passover covenant meal? Explain.

The early Church retained the Old Testament understanding of remembrance as a participation and called this sacrament "the breaking of bread."

35 Turn to **1 Corinthians 10:16-17.** What does St. Paul teach about the Eucharist?

What the Church says

" It is the spirit that quickens, the flesh profits nothing: that is to say, 'You ought to understand My words in a spiritual sense: he who understands them carnally is profited nothing.' To interpret carnally is to take a proposition in its bare literal meaning, and allow no other. But we should not judge of mysteries in this way; but examine them with the inward eye; i.e. understand them spiritually. It was carnal to doubt how our Lord could give His flesh to eat. What then? Is it not real flesh? Yes, verily. In saying then that the flesh profits nothing, He does not speak of His own flesh, but that of the carnal hearer of His word. "

— **St. John Chrysostom,** on John 6:63

The sacrifice of Christ and the sacrifice of the Eucharist are one single sacrifice: "The victim is one and the same: the same now offers through the ministry of priests, who then offered himself on the cross; only the manner of offering is different." "In this divine sacrifice which is celebrated in the Mass, the same Christ who offered himself once in a bloody manner on the altar of the cross is contained and is offered in an unbloody manner" (CCC 1367).[3]

That the Eucharist is merely symbolic and not the literal presence of Christ is a heresy that became prevalent around AD 1500. The Catholic Church has preserved and taught the "real presence" since the apostles' time.

36 What else does St. Paul teach about the Eucharist in **1 Corinthians 11:27-32?**

The fulfillment and interpretation of all Old Testament bread, Jesus is present. He feeds us. This bread is better than manna because we can live forever with God by becoming one with, eating, this Presence Bread.

3   Council of Trent (1562): *Doctrina de ss. Missae sacrificio,* c. 2: DS 1743; cf. Hebrews 9:14, 27.

LET'S REVIEW

- Through numerous Old Testament types, especially the miraculous daily manna and Presence Bread in the Tabernacle, God prepared his people for the Presence Bread of Life in Christ offered daily for the Church.

- In order to be a true antitype, a thing must be in all ways greater; therefore, none of the New Testament fulfillments of Old Testament bread can be merely physical or simply symbolic. The Lord's Supper must communicate grace and therefore eternal life.

- Jesus said the Eucharist is supernatural bread, not symbolic bread.

- Receiving the Eucharist is a participation in the Body and Blood of Christ (see 1 Corinthians 10:16) and therefore real and true, eternal Presence Bread.

- Receiving the Eucharist unworthily makes one "guilty of profaning the body and blood of the Lord" (1 Corinthians 11:27).

- Because Jesus' flesh and blood are resurrected and alive, he stipulated that we must eat his flesh and drink his blood or we cannot also have eternal life (see John 6:53-58).

- The Catholic Church has wholly maintained Jesus' teaching on his real presence in the Eucharist since the Apostles.

YOU ARE NOW READY FOR THE **SESSION THREE VIDEO**.

STEP 2:
VIDEO PRESENTATION

Session Three: The Bread of Life

- God desires unity

- The super-marital sacrament of union

- Eucharist as sacrament of unity, communion

- Jesus does not become one with us, we become one with him

- Not discerning Body of Christ is deadly

- Why the Church withholds Eucharist from non-Catholics

    – Guests in the bedroom

    – Church takes the long view

STEP 3:
SMALL-GROUP DISCUSSION

INVITATION

The Catholic Church has wholly maintained Jesus' teaching on his real presence in the Eucharist since the Apostles. Other Christian churches watered down the purity of the Scripture teaching or abandoned it entirely in designating it a mere symbol. Our Holy Eucharist is in the presence of God through Christ, but also is eternally the presence of God, tabernacling with us in, with, and through Christ in his Church. The Eucharist is the consistent continuation of God's command that there be perpetual Presence Bread in the Tabernacle.

Notes

_____

_____

_____

_____

_____

_____

_____

_____

_____

_____

_____

_____

GOD PROMPT – LOVE THE WORD™

LISTEN: "Give us this day our daily bread" (Matthew 6:11).

OBSERVE: How does God's daily provision of bread for his people in the wilderness make you more confident of his provision for you today in your life and circumstance?

Have you ever experienced a drastic change in financial circumstances? Have you ever been "hungry"?

What, if anything, did you learn through that experience?

When have you been spiritually hungry?

What assurance can you have after this chapter, about God satisfying that hunger?

Pray and ask God to identify one or more statements or Bible passages from this chapter that he wants you to understand, memorize, or practice. Perhaps you would like to underline it (or them).

VERBALIZE: Lord, the most meaningful statement or Bible passage through which you spoke to me in this chapter was ...

Lord, my biggest hang-up about the Eucharist is ...

I believe that in response to my reading in this chapter, you want me to ...

As I think about my problem, challenge, or circumstance, I need your provision here ...

When I think about the care with which you provide for your people, I feel ...

I need your help to ...

 ENTRUST: *Lord, I believe it is your desire to feed all my hungers. Thank you for being present with me through the Eucharist. Thank you for feeding me with the bread and wine of your Body and Blood. I am not worthy that you should enter under my roof, but only say the word and my soul shall be healed. Amen.*

Holy Smoke

O Sacred Heart of Jesus, for whom it is impossible not to have compassion on the afflicted, have pity on us miserable sinners and grant us the grace which we ask of you, through the Sorrowful and Immaculate Heart of Mary, your tender Mother and ours. Amen.

STEP 1: HOME PREPARATION

Whose great idea was it to combine liturgy, incense, and prayer? It was God's!

OLD TESTAMENT INCENSE

Nestled in the quiet glow of the Holy Place, just beyond the golden lampstand and the Table of Presence Bread in the Temple, rested the golden incense altar. Like the Table of Presence Bread, the incense altar had a golden crown decorating the top. Please turn to **Exodus 30:1-10** and read the description of the incense altar.

1 What was it made of?

2 Where was it positioned?

About eighteen inches square and three feet high, this smaller altar was a stand used to burn incense in the Holy Place. Like the Ark of the Covenant, the Table of Presence Bread, and the bronze altar, this altar was made of acacia wood, a wood similar to cedar. But unlike the bronze altar, it was overlaid with gold: bronze for judgment, gold for divinity.

3 What do you think this difference might mean?

KEY SCRIPTURE

"The prayer of a righteous man has great power in its effects."

— **James 5:16**

As with other instruments in the Tabernacle, rings and poles were used to carry this altar when the Israelites traveled through the wilderness. A curious thing about the incense altar, like the bronze altar, was the inclusion of horns at each corner. (Look back to Part One if needed, or the back of this workbook for answers if you have not yet participated in Part One.)

4   What did the horns symbolize?

5   What interesting thing happened to the horns once a year? (See **Exodus 30:10.**)

6   What was the schedule for burning incense?

7   When was the incense ritual to cease?

This sweet incense was to be burned daily upon the golden altar at the offering of every sacrifice so that a cloud of smoke might fill the inner chamber at the "hour of incense," the moment when the sacrificial blood was sprinkled.

The incense on the altar was burned from the original fire taken from the bronze altar of sacrifice. Both fires were to be eternal flames originating from God.

8 ▸ Does this bring any clarity to **Luke 1:8-12** for you? Explain.

What the Church says

9 ▸ Turn now to **Exodus 37:29.** What highly skilled craftsman's responsibility was it to make the incense and the holy anointing oil?

10 ▸ We find the divine recipe for the incense in **Exodus 30:34-38.** In the space below, record the details that seem most significant to you about the incense.

" *For me, prayer is a surge of the heart; it is a simple look turned toward heaven, it is a cry of recognition and of love, embracing both trial and joy.* "

— **CCC 2558,**
quoting St. Thérèse of Lisieux, *Autobiographical Manuscript,* C 25

11 ▸ Do you recognize any of the ingredients?

Salt was an ancient preservative and antiseptic. Another ingredient in the Tabernacle incense that might be familiar is frankincense. It is thought that the word originally indicated incense obtained from the Franks (now France).

12 ▸ What was frankincense used for in **Matthew 2:11?**

Frankincense and myrrh are often associated together in Scripture. Both are balsams, basically plant sap. Because of their extreme expense, they were among the gifts brought to Jesus by the Magi.

The significance of frankincense in the Tabernacle incense, both in the incense altar and its use with the Presence Bread, is even more interesting.

13 Indicate the special significance Scripture gives to incense in **Psalm 141:2.**

The connection between prayer and incense is echoed in the New Testament, too.

NEW TESTAMENT INCENSE

The Prayers of the High Priest

In the Gospel of John, we get a glimpse into Jesus' life of sacrificial prayer.

14 Please read through **John 17.** Can you discern from the first verse why it is called the Prayer of the Hour of Jesus?

15 It is also sometimes called the "priestly" prayer of Jesus. What are your thoughts on that designation?

It was one of Jesus' last prayers on earth. In it he summarizes all of creation and salvation: God and the world, the Word and the flesh, eternal life and time, the love that hands itself over and the sin that betrays it, the disciples present and those who will believe in him by their word, and humiliation and glory. It is a prayer of beautiful unity, the continuation of an entire life of previous prayer. Truly, its depths exude the fragrance of incense.

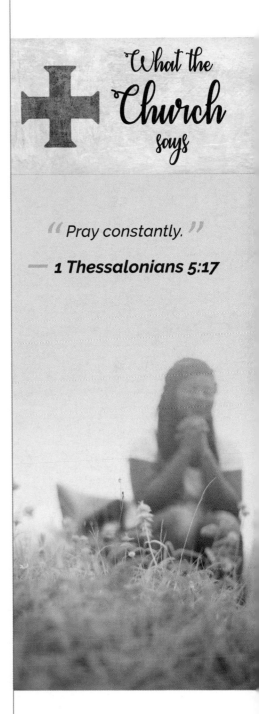

What the Church says

" *Pray constantly.* "

— *1 Thessalonians 5:17*

16 What part of this prayer touches you the most? Explain.

17 What part do you consider the most sacrificial? Why?

18 Jesus' two very last prayers crown his prayer life. Turn to **Matthew 27:46.** You might have to look for it, but somewhere in your Bible you should have a reference related to this verse. What is the reference?

" *[Jesus] prays for us as our priest, prays in us as our Head, and is prayed to by us as our God. Therefore let us acknowledge our voice in him and his in us.* "

— **CCC 2616,**
quoting St. Augustine, *Enarratio in Psalmum,* 85: CCL 39, 1176

19 Yes, Jesus prays **Psalm 22.** Turn there and compare it to Jesus' words.

20 Take a look, now, at **Luke 23:46.** You should also have a reference to another verse in your Bible. What is it?

21 Jesus' last prayer is **Psalm 31:5.** Turn there and compare the two passages in the space below.

San Agustin by Antonio Rodríguez
(1636–1691)

22 › Given what you know about the incense altar and the hour of incense, and how King David viewed his own prayers, why do you think Jesus prayed the psalms during his passion, the most difficult, sacrificial moments of his life?

INCENSE IN THE CHURCH

The Daily Office in the Early Church

As a Jew, Jesus would have participated in the fixed-hour prayer tradition of Judaism. He would have been so familiar with it as to have memorized many of the prayers, many of which were psalms. These prayers helped him through his agony on the Cross.

23 › Turn to **Psalm 119:164.** How many times a day did the psalmist himself pray?

24 › Following the example of Jesus, the early Church also prayed fixed-hour prayer. Turn to **Acts 3:1-10.** The healing of the lame man on the Temple steps by Saints Peter and John is the first detailed miracle of the apostolic Church. Where were they headed at the time (**verse 1**)?

25 › Two devout Jews, now Christians, were on their way to ninth-hour (three o'clock) prayer. Soon after the healing miracle, one of the most defining moments of Christianity occurred. Turn to **Acts 10:9-16.** St. Peter's vision of the sheet descending with both clean and unclean animals occurred at noon on a rooftop. What had St. Peter gone there to observe?

God's instruction to Peter to accept all that God had created as clean was given during Peter's regular noon devotion. God spoke to him on the roof, however, not by some accident of having been in that spot when the noon bell caught him, but because he was accustomed to set aside hours through his ancestral prayer discipline.

The Jewish practice of fixed-hour prayer on the twelves, threes, sixes, and nines of every day was continued through Jesus and the apostles into the Church. We know that the apostles were in the habit of including the psalms in their prayers.

26 Turn to **Acts 4:23-30.** Can you find the reference to the psalm they prayed in this passage? Turn there and compare the passages in the space below.

To this day, the psalms remain the living center of the Divine Office, the Church's daily prayers. Here, "office" means "duty," "trust," or "authority."

Somewhere, every hour, in every time zone, in every country on the globe, God's people are offering prayers to him.

The Lord's Prayer

Turn to **Matthew 6:9-13.** It was Jesus who also taught us to pray the Our Father. In obedience to him, the first early Church manual of Christian practice, called *The Teaching of the Twelve Apostles,* or the *Didache,* taught that followers of Jesus should pray the Lord's Prayer at least three times each day. The habit expanded quickly throughout the Church to include all the "offices" or hours of prayer. The prayers of the Church are not "vain repetitions," then, but imitate the apostles in obedience to Christ.

Prayers of the Church Triumphant

Even the Church in heaven offers "incense." The book of Revelation, written by St. John, gives us a privileged view into the worship occurring in heaven right now.

27 ▸ Please turn to **Revelation 5:8-10.** Imagine it. How are the prayers of the Church described here?

28 ▸ And to whom are they praying?

> " 'Fiat': this is Christian prayer: to be wholly God's, because he is wholly ours. "
>
> — **CCC 2617**

29 ▸ What more do we learn about our prayers, especially those of the martyrs, in **Revelation 8:3-5?**

These passages in Revelation show us the golden incense altar before the eternal throne of God in heaven right now (Revelation 8:3). Beside the fire burning on it stands an angel burning incense, "the prayers of all the saints." This prayer described as incense is eternally present in the heavenly tabernacle, just as God commanded in the Old Testament Tabernacle.

30 ▸ How does it feel to know your prayers are eternally before God?

Gethsemane II by Carl Heinrich Bloch (1636–1691)

31 Like the Old Testament Tabernacle's incense altar, the heavenly incense altar is adorned with what four appendages in **Revelation 9:13?**

Through John's vision in the book of Revelation, we see the Old Testament incense altar was merely a copy of the one in heaven. The inclusion of the incense altar in the Tabernacle was meant to communicate and foreshadow the prayer that surrounds God in his heavenly tabernacle. But the incense of prayer in the Tabernacle would not be limited to Jews. In the Church, the Gentiles (non-Jews) would offer incense, too.

32 Please turn to **Malachi 1:11.** This is an Old Testament prophecy of the time when Gentiles would offer holy sacrifices to the Lord. What would accompany that "pure offering?"

33 Jesus affirmed this prophecy in **Mark 11:15-17.** How do you think Jesus' statement might relate to Malachi's prophecy?

For the People of God, the Temple was to be the place of their education in prayer: pilgrimages, feasts and sacrifices, the evening offering, the incense, and the Presence Bread ("shewbread") – all these signs of the holiness and glory of God Most High and Most Near were appeals to and ways of prayer (CCC 2581).

The Catholic Church uses incense during the Mass in accordance with Revelation and the prophecies of Malachi. Through our incense and prayer, the binding Old Testament command to burn incense forever as a salt covenant in the Tabernacle remains valid and perpetual.

In the Catholic Mass, the highest form of Christian prayer, the smoke of incense symbolizes the prayers of the faithful drifting up to join those in heaven, and it represents the purification of everything the "incense" of sacrificial prayer touches. Incense creates the ambiance of heaven. It adds a sense of solemnity and mystery to the Mass as it evokes the vision of Revelation. The scent and smoke remind us of the transcendence of the Mass, which links heaven with earth, and help us to enter into the presence of God.

LET'S REVIEW

This is why the Church uses incense in the Liturgy:

- God commanded the use of incense with the daily sacrifices in the Old Testament Tabernacle and that the practice should remain forever.

- Scripture prophesies that non-Jews will offer a daily, "pure offering" with incense "in every place" (see Malachi 1:11).

- The Catholic Mass is the highest form of prayer and the "source and summit of the Christian life" (CCC 1324),[4] as it is a participation in the heavenly liturgy.

- The Catholic Church combines liturgy, incense, and prayer with the only pure, sacrificial offering possible: that of Jesus' own Body and Blood.

YOU ARE NOW READY FOR THE **SESSION FOUR VIDEO**.

---

[4] *Lumen gentium* (LG) 11.

STEP 2:
VIDEO PRESENTATION

Session Four: Holy Smoke

- A pleasing aroma, Tabernacle incense, and anointing oil (Exodus 30:22-33)

- Divine recipe: salt and myrrh

- Only holy fire

- Anointed furnishings and priests

- Trinity of suffering

  – God the Father

  – God the Son

    ○ Jesus' birth (Matthew 2:11)

    ○ Jesus' cross (Mark 15:23)

    ○ Jesus' burial (John 19:39)

  – God the Holy Spirit (Revelation 2:8-10)

- Communion with man (Ruth 1:20-21)

- Suffering draws us closer to God

STEP 3:
SMALL-GROUP DISCUSSION

INVITATION

Our Catholic prayer tradition is very rich, rooted in Christ, and backed by the full power of the Church—all the angels and saints and the Church militant all over the world. As the horns on the incense altar indicate, it is sacrificial and very powerful and authoritative.

Notes

_____

_____

_____

_____

_____

_____

_____

_____

_____

_____

_____

_____

_____

_____

GOD PROMPT – LOVE THE WORD™

 LISTEN: "And he taught, and said to them, 'Is it not written, 'My house shall be called a house of prayer for all the nations'? But you have made it a den of robbers" (Mark 11:17).

 OBSERVE: What robs your prayer time?

When do you find it difficult to pray?

Consider how precious and potent your prayer is when you offer it as a sacrifice in those moments. What comes to mind?

What was the most sacrificial prayer you remember ever praying?

Over and over, Scripture tells us Jesus prayed through the night or went alone to the desert or to the mountain to pray. Where do you pray best?

How is your prayer like incense, "a sweet fragrance" before the Lord?

Do you think about your prayers rising to God as you attend Mass?

 VERBALIZE: Lord, the most meaningful passage of Scripture through which you spoke to me today was …

Lord, I believe that in response to today's study, you want me to …

As I think about my relationship to the priesthood and with priests I have known …

I need your help to …

ENTRUST: *Take our prayers into the sanctuary of heaven and enable them to make our peace with God. Holy Mary, help the miserable, strengthen the discouraged, comfort the sorrowful, pray for your people, plead for the clergy, intercede for all women consecrated to God. May all who venerate you feel now your help and protection. Be ready to help us when we pray, and bring back to us the answers to our prayers. Amen.*

Holy of Holies

Angel of God, my guardian dear, to whom God's love commits me here,
ever this day, be at my side, to light and guard, rule and guide. Amen.

STEP 1: HOME PREPARATION

Have you ever seen those huge, incredibly thick, embroidered tapestries that hang in European country homes and old castles? They're more like rugs, really, and I often wonder how long it must have taken to weave and embroider such large tapestries.

OLD TESTAMENT TABERNACLE VEIL

The Tabernacle included something similar. At the entrance to the Tabernacle sanctuary hung a protective curtain that kept out the courtyard's sand, heat, flies, and dirt.

But there was a second, more interior curtain that screened the inner chamber of the Old Testament Tabernacle. This innermost chamber of the Holy Place was called the Most Holy Place, or the Holy of Holies. Similar to "King of Kings" and "Lord of Lords," the language is superlative. Just as "King of Kings" means that Jesus is the King of all kings, "Holy of Holies" means this place is the holiest of all places.

The Holy of Holies held the most important object in the Tabernacle. The area was so secret, it was completely secluded and partitioned off even from the Holy Place, which was itself partitioned off from the Tabernacle court. In fact, the word "holy" actually means "separate" or "set apart," so this area was the most set apart, distinct place on earth.

1 Turn to **Exodus 26:31-35.** Of what was this tapestry made?

2 Which direction did it face? You may need to review the Tabernacle diagram in Part One. (See the back of this workbook for the answer if you have not yet participated in Part One).

3 Compare that direction with **Matthew 24:27.**

KEY SCRIPTURE

"*For thou didst form my inward parts, thou didst knit me together in my mother's womb.*"

— *Psalm 139:13*

The most beautifully intricate of all the Tabernacle fabrics, the innermost veil hung by clasps from pillars, dividing the Holy Place into two separate rooms. All the objects in immediate contact with the Holy Place were of gold or silver, but the sockets of the pillars supporting the veil or screen were bronze, so they must have been some distance from the framework. The fibers of the veils were twisted for greater strength, and the curtain and secret chamber illustrated how ill-fitted the children of Israel and even the priests were for the immediate intimacy of heaven.

4 ▸ What design was woven into the texture of the Tabernacle curtain?

5 ▸ Turn to **Genesis 3:24.** What were they doing in this verse?

6 What do you think might be the significance of that fact in relation to the Tabernacle veil?

7 What was done with the veil when the Tabernacle journeyed with the Israelites through the wilderness? (See **Numbers 4:5.**)

8 What colors were used to make the veil? (See **Exodus 26:31.**)

> The body is a " woven " veil hiding the soul, the most secret and holy place of a person's being.

Purple, the most precious of the ancient dyes, was the color of royalty. Since blue was associated with the sky, it came to symbolize the heavens. In Scripture, red, sometimes called "scarlet," is symbolic of blood.

Even more fascinating than the colors used, however, is the word used to describe the veil in **Exodus 40:21**; in Hebrew, it is *sakak*, translated twice in this verse as "screen(ed)." It is sometimes also translated in Scripture as "covered," "woven," or "knit." This word is used almost exclusively in the Old Testament to describe the veiling of the presence of God from human eyes in the Holy of Holies. So a woven veil covered the presence of God.

This word appears once again, however, in another intriguing place. Turn to **Psalm 139** and read through it.

9 What part of this psalm speaks to you the most? Explain.

10 Below, please identify and circle where you believe the Hebrew word *sakak* is used in **Psalm 139:13.**

"For thou didst form my inward parts, thou didst knit me together in my mother's womb."

The same term used in Scripture to describe the intricately woven Tabernacle veil is used by the psalmist to describe his own flesh. The Tabernacle veil was covered in cherubim, and it screened the Holy of Holies, the presence of God resting in the mysterious cloud, from human eyes.

The psalmist states, then, in the most delicate poetry, that his body, your body, was prepared to veil the presence of God—that one day each one's anatomy should become the temple of God. The flesh is the holy preparation of God.

NEW TESTAMENT VEIL

11 Jesus understood this very well. What does he say in **John 2:19-22?**

12 What is hidden by the "veil" of Jesus' flesh in **Luke 9:28-36?**

13 What are some instances in the Bible in which Jesus was "guarded" or accompanied by angels?

What the Church says

" *There was then so clear a change made from the Law to the Gospel, from the Synagogue to the Church, from the many sacrifices to the One Victim, God Himself, that when our Lord gave up the ghost the veil was violently and suddenly rent asunder.* "

— **St. Leo,**
Serm. xvii. *de Pass*

14 What about yourself? See also **Matthew 18:10.**

15 What does this reality require of us in working for a culture of life from conception to natural death?

" I esteem it, O my God, an inestimable benefit, that thou hast granted me an angel to guide me from the moment of my birth, to my death. "

— St. Augustine,
De dilig. Deo. Medit. chap. xii

16 Turn to **Matthew 27:46-51.** In the agony of his passion, what happens just after Jesus quotes Psalm 22:1, "My God, my God, why hast thou forsaken me?"

17 Jesus' veil of flesh screened the presence of God in him from human eyes. His precious body was rent by the torturous passion just before the veil in the stone Temple in Jerusalem that symbolized him was rent in two from top to bottom. In the space below, compare this event with what the author of Hebrews says of this incident in **Hebrews 9.**

San Agustin by Antonio Rodriguez
(1636–1691)

Origen, an early Christian theologian, said,

> It is understood that there were two veils; one veiling the Holy of Holies, the other, the outer part of the tabernacle or temple. In the Passion then of our Lord and Saviour, it was the outer veil which

was rent from the top to the bottom, that by the rending of the veil from the beginning to the end of the world, the mysteries might be published which had been hid with good reason until the Lord's coming. "But when that which is perfect is come," (1 Cor. 13:10) then the second veil also shall be taken away, that we may see the things that are hidden within, to wit, the true Ark of the Testament, and behold the Cherubim and the rest in their real nature.[5]

18 In the previous quote, Origen himself quotes **1 Corinthians 13:10.** Turn there and read through **verse 12.** What does Origen mean when he quotes **verse 10** above?

19 The Church follows Christ in all things. What, if anything, do you think it means for the body of Christ, the Church, that the veil of Jesus' flesh was rent?

Take a look at **Ezekiel 44:1-3.** Although this passage speaks of the entrance gate to the outer part of the Tabernacle and does not mention a veil, the idea of being "enclosed" or "screened" is the same, and it is one we will revisit in the next session. Compare this passage to these quotes from two of our Church Fathers, Saints Ambrose and Augustine:

> Who is this gate, if not Mary? Is it not closed because she is a virgin? Mary is the gate through which Christ entered this world, when He was brought forth in the virginal birth and the manner of His birth did not break the seals of virginity.[6]

> It is written (Ezech. 44:2): "This gate shall be shut, it shall not be opened, and no man shall pass through it; because the Lord the God of Israel hath entered in by it....What means this closed gate in the House of the Lord, except that Mary is to be ever inviolate? What does it mean that "no man shall pass through it," save that Joseph shall not know her? And what is this—"The Lord alone enters in and goeth out

---

[5]   Origen's thoughts on Matthew 27:51, quoted in Aquinas, *Catena Aurea: Commentary on the Four Gospels.*

[6]   St. Ambrose, *De institutione virginis.*

Detail of fresco, Sistine Chapel by Michelangelo Buonarroti (c. 1508–1512)

by it"—except that the Holy Ghost shall impregnate her, and that the Lord of angels shall be born of her? And what means this—"It shall be shut for evermore"—but that Mary is a virgin before His Birth, a virgin in His Birth, and a virgin after His Birth?[7]

20 What connections can you make between the veil in the Tabernacle and the closed gate of **Ezekiel 44?**

LET'S REVIEW

This is why the Church guards the sanctity of life from cradle to grave:

- The most sacred place on the face of the earth in the Old Testament was the Holy of Holies, the innermost chamber of the Tabernacle.

- The Holy of Holies was shrouded by a veil to protect the mysterious secrecy and sacredness where God's presence dwelt.

- The Tabernacle veil was used to wrap the Ark of the Covenant for protection when the Israelites journeyed through the wilderness.

- The words used in describing the delicate weaving of the veil are used to describe how God weaves the flesh as a screen for the human soul.

- Jesus said his body is a temple.

- Scripture says my body is a temple.

- The body is a veil for the "holy of holies" of the soul.

- The Catholic Church is the only Christian church that still follows apostolic teaching on life issues from cradle to grave.

YOU ARE NOW READY FOR THE **SESSION FIVE VIDEO.**

---

7   Thomas Aquinas, *Summa Theologica* 3.28.3, quoting Augustine, *De Annunt. Dom. iii.*

STEP 2:
VIDEO PRESENTATION

Session Five: Holy of Holies

- All of creation serves him

- Scarlet

    A. Color for priestly vestments and veil in the Tabernacle

    B. Symbolic of blood

        1. Rahab's string (Joshua 2:18-21)

        2. Red tent legend

        3. Robe put on Christ (Matthew 27:28)

        4. Whore of Babylon's beast, her garments, and her people (Revelation 17:3-4, 18)

    C. Symbolic of martyrdom

    D. Cross

        1. "I am a worm ... despised by the people" (Psalm 22:6)

        2. Jesus quotes from the Cross (Matthew 27:46)

- Tola worm

    A. Red, soft-scaled insect

    B. Attaches itself to tree and dies

    C. Body crushed for red dye

    D. Holy of Holies and Priesthood only through blood

STEP 3:
SMALL-GROUP DISCUSSION

INVITATION

In his encyclical letter *Redemptor Hominis,* St. John Paul II taught about the dignity that God invested in human flesh. Through his redemption in Christ, man becomes a new creature:

> In this dimension man finds again the greatness, dignity and value that belong to his humanity. In the mystery of the Redemption man becomes newly "expressed" and, in a way, is newly created.[8]

The Catechism also teaches this, as explained by Carl Olson, a contemporary Catholic writer:

> By entering into human history and uniting himself with mankind, God not only restored communion between the divine and the natural, he modeled divine sonship for us. By becoming united to humanity, he demonstrated that man can become one with God. Man can become by grace what the Son is by nature. Put another way, the Son of God became a Son of Man so that men might become sons of God (see CCC 460).[9]

Notes

_____

_____

_____

_____

_____

_____

_____

_____

_____

_____

_____

_____

[8] John Paul II, *Redemptor Hominis* 10.

[9] Carl E. Olson, "The Dignity of the Human Person: Pope John Paul II's Teaching on Divinization in the Trinitarian Encyclicals," *Saint Austin Review* (2002), discussing CCC 460.

GOD PROMPT – LOVE THE WORD™

 LISTEN: "Do you not know that your body is the temple of the Holy Spirit within you, which you have from God? You are not your own; you were bought with a price. So glorify God in your body" (1 Corinthians 6:19-20).

 OBSERVE: Remembering that the Tabernacle veil was beautifully embroidered with cherubim, what is God saying to you about your own body?

Human anatomy screens the presence of God in the soul from ordinary eyes. Does this fact make you see others you meet in the marketplace differently?

St. Teresa of Calcutta spoke repeatedly about Jesus in "distressing disguise." While she spoke specifically of the poor, it is also true of other things. Who in your life is currently most distressing to you?

How could this person be Jesus in disguise?

 VERBALIZE: Lord, the most meaningful statement or passage of Scripture through which you spoke to me in this chapter was ...

Lord, I believe that in response to my reading in this chapter, you want me to ...

I need your help to see you in this distressing disguise ...

When I think about people that I dislike, and that you are hidden in them, I feel you saying you want me to ...

 ENTRUST: *O Lord, thou hast searched me and known me. Thou knowest when I sit down and when I rise up; thou discernest my thoughts from afar. Thou searchest out my path and my lying down, and art acquainted with all my ways. Even before a word is on my tongue, lo, O Lord, thou know it altogether ... For thou didst form my inward parts, thou didst knit me together in my mother's womb. I praise thee, for thou art fearful and wonderful. Wonderful are thy works!" (Psalm 139:1-4, 13-14).*

The Throne of God

Spirit of wisdom and understanding, enlighten our minds to perceive the mysteries of the universe in relation to eternity. Spirit of God, spark our faith, hope, and love into new action each day. Fill our lives with wonder and awe in your presence, which penetrates all creation. Amen.

STEP 1:
HOME PREPARATION

Among the things I love about the Catholic Church is the way it preserves and protects the mysteries of the Faith by refusing to attempt an explanation of subjects that require faith to savor. The secret interior of the Holy of Holies is one of those profound mysteries. In this session, we are going to explore the connection between the Old Testament Ark of the Covenant in the Holy of Holies and Mary, the Mother of God.

THE OLD TESTAMENT ARK OF THE COVENANT

Resting behind the veil within the beautiful cocoon of the innermost chamber of the Holy Place was the most important religious object associated with the Tabernacle. The dimensions of the Holy of Holies made it a perfect cube, a geometric stipulation we see repeated in Ezekiel's prophetic vision of the New Testament temple.

1 **Exodus 25:10-22** relates the mysterious contents of the Holy of Holies. What was inside the dark little room behind the veil where the presence of God dwelt?

2 What was this "box" made of?

3 With what was the Ark plated, inside and out?

4 | Wood is symbolic of man, while gold is symbolic of deity. What does this suggest about the special "box," called the "Ark"?

5 | The dimensions of the Ark, converted, would amount to about four feet long by two and a half feet wide. Several other facilities in the Tabernacle also included poles and rings. What were the poles and rings for?

The stipulations were clear that no man was to touch the Ark directly. The poles and rings allowed it to be transported safely without being touched.

6 | What was the lid of the Ark called (**verse 17**)?

7 | **Leviticus 16** describes the Day of Atonement, the highest holy day of the Israelite year. In the definition provided below, please circle any of the possible meanings and implications of the word "atonement" that interest you:

> **Atonement:** *transliteration: kâphar, pronunciation: kaw-far'*
> *To cover; to expiate or condone, to placate or cancel: - appease,*
> *make (an) atonement, cleanse, disannul, forgive, be merciful,*
> *pacify, pardon, to pitch, purge (away), put off, (make) reconcile*
> *(reconciliation).*[10]

Only on the Day of Atonement was anyone allowed inside the Holy of Holies, and even then, only the high priest could enter. (See Leviticus 16:2-3.)

8 | What was the high priest told to do to the mercy seat on this day? (See **Leviticus 16:14-16.**)

The Holy of Holies was the sleeping place for young Samuel, later the prophet.

---

[10] *Strong's Hebrew Lexicon #3722.*

Little gold bells on the hem of the high priest's vestments tinkled as the priest entered the Presence of God in the Holy of Holies on the Day of Atonement, letting the people know he had not died of sacrilege while serving on their behalf.

9 ▸ The Ark of the Covenant was where satisfaction for sin was made on behalf of the whole people of God for the entire year. Explain why it makes sense that it was called the mercy seat.

Because they illustrated God's mercy, the Ark and Day of Atonement held a meaning similar to the Christian Cross for the ancient Hebrews.

10 ▸ Return now to **Exodus 25:17-20.** What was the mercy seat made of?

11 ▸ What images covered the mercy seat?

According to the first commandment, images were completely forbidden among the people of Israel. Remember that they had spent several hundred years in pagan Egypt, where idol worship was a regular practice. The purpose of the wilderness journey was to teach them how to worship God solely and properly before they entered their Promised Land. Only then would they know how to prosper in their new land. The two golden cherubim covering the mercy seat on the Ark were an exception to this commandment of God against such images.

12 ▸ What does the exception suggest to you about the Ark?

The Mercy Seat, illustration from 1890 Holman Bible

In the previous session, we explored the significance of cherubim on the veil screening the Holy of Holies. Note how these cherubim surrounded the Holy of Holies as they were both embroidered on the veil and depicted on the mercy seat of the Tabernacle.

13 It is also noteworthy that the word translated "ark" actually means "coffin." What, if anything, does that knowledge add to your understanding of the Ark?

14 Later in Hebrew history, the Ark came to be regarded as the "Oracle." According to **Exodus 25:22,** why is this so?

15 Do you think it was an audible voice that proceeded from the presence of God on the mercy seat? Explain.

16 Do you think this presence was literal or symbolic? Explain.

17 What was one important item contained in the Ark, mentioned in **Exodus 25:16?**

Depending on your translation, this item is sometimes also called the "Commandment" or "Word of the Lord."

What the Church says

" *You shall not make for yourself a graven image, or any likeness of anything that is in heaven above, or that is in the earth beneath, or that is in the water under the earth; you shall not bow down to them or serve them; for I the LORD your God am a jealous God.* "

— **Exodus 20:4-5**

18 We echo this idea at every Mass when we say, "The Word of the Lord." What do we understand the "Word" to be in this context?

19 According to **Exodus 16:33** and **Numbers 17:10,** what other contents were included in the Ark?

20 Can you recall the three items in the Ark? (See **Hebrews 9:3-5.**) List them here.

We will look at them again in a moment, but these tangible reminders of God's tender provision for his beloved people were to remain before the Lord in the Holy of Holies forever. As in all things, Jesus makes it possible to fulfill God's command "forever." Jesus brings all Old Testament types forward into his Church.

JESUS AS NEW COVENANT

21 Look at **Romans 3:24-25** below in which St. Paul says God sent Jesus to do something for us. What was it?

"[We] are justified by his grace as a gift, through the redemption which is in Christ Jesus, whom God put forward as an *expiation* by his blood, to be received by faith. This was to show God's righteousness, because in his divine forbearance he had passed over former sins" (Romans 3:24-25, emphasis added).

The word "expiation" is the same word translated elsewhere as "mercy seat." Jesus is the new mercy seat, the place where the blood of atonement is poured out and sin is atoned for. At this point in our study of the Tabernacle, you should be very familiar with how Jesus also fulfills the contents of the Ark, too.

22 How is Jesus the new Manna?

23 How is Jesus the new Rod of Aaron?

24 How is Jesus the final "Testimony" or Covenant?

As both God and man, Jesus by his blood makes atonement for the heavy cost of all human sin. Thus, he is our mercy seat, the place where God's presence rests. Jesus is our Eucharist, and so he is the new Manna, the Bread of Life. He is our High Priest and the final Command or Word of God. Yet another sublime truth about the Ark begins with his mother, Mary.

MARY AS ARK OF THE NEW COVENANT

25 Compare the following passages. In each one, notice the way the Holy Spirit is described and what he is doing. Note any thoughts that come to mind in the space provided.

Genesis 1:2-3 –

Exodus 40:34-35 –

Luke 1:35 –

The same creative, speaking Holy Spirit "moving" on the face of the Genesis waters is the Spirit, or "breath," that rested on the mercy seat of the Ark. The Spirit filled the Tabernacle and gave life to the Israelites through all he spoke to Moses.

The same Spirit "overshadowed" the Virgin Mary and generated new life, the Word, in her womb. Just as the Tabernacle Ark held the manna, the rod of Aaron, and the Word of God, Mary was the first to carry within her the new Manna, new Rod of Aaron, and final Word of God. Like the Ark, she was visited by angels, and her purity was untouched by men in fulfillment of Ezekiel's prophecy of the closed gate of the new temple (Ezekiel 44:1-3).

We see the connection between Mary and the Old Testament Tabernacle Ark affirmed in the heavenly tabernacle, too. Turn to **Revelation 11:19–12:1.** Throughout salvation history, important revelations of God were frequently accompanied by great signs like thunder, lightning, noise, and even hail. Remember Mount Sinai?

26 ▸ When the heavenly tabernacle was opened, what did St. John see there (**Revelation 11:19**)?

27 ▸ Notice the first word of **Revelation 12:1.** How does this word point back to the previous verse?

Translators include them for convenience, but remember that the first Scripture writings did not include punctuation, chapter or verse numbers, or paragraph separations. We know these two verses are actually a pair because of the transition word used to link them.

28 ▸ Who then is this woman, this Ark who gave birth to the prophetic child (**Revelation 12:13**)?

Mary, in whom the Lord himself has just made his dwelling, is the daughter of Zion in person, the ark of the covenant, the place where the glory of the Lord dwells. She is "the dwelling of God ... with men." Full of grace, Mary is wholly given over to him who has come to dwell in her and whom she is about to give to the world (CCC 2676, quoting Revelation 21:3).

The Ark of the Covenant in the Old Testament was eventually lost to the Israelites. According to Jewish teaching in 2 Maccabees 2:4-8, the prophet Jeremiah concealed it until the coming of the Messiah when it would again be revealed by God.

The Church Fathers understood that reappearance of the Ark to refer to Mary herself, the woman who appears as the Ark in the heavenly temple in Revelation 11:19–12:2. These parallels and many more moved the early Church to regard Mary as the new Ark and inspired them to give her the title "Ark of the New Covenant" in their writings.

LET'S REVIEW

The Catholic Church venerates Mary as the ark of the New Covenant and great sign of the Church because:

- The Ark of the Covenant in the Tabernacle was the place where God's presence dwelt.

- Inside the Ark were symbols of the Old Covenant, all meant to be eternal and fulfilled in Christ.

- Jesus is the New Covenant; Mary carried the New Covenant in her womb and is therefore the new ark.

- In the heavenly temple, the ark is a woman, a queen, who gives birth to a male child who is the King (see Revelation 11:19–12:2).

- In addition to Israel or Zion, the Church has always understood the ark in the heavenly temple to be Mary.

- As the ark of the New Covenant, Mary is the great sign and forerunner of the Church.

YOU ARE NOW READY FOR THE **SESSION SIX VIDEO.**

STEP 2:
VIDEO PRESENTATION

Session Six: The Throne of God

- New Ark

- Noah's ark of salvation (Genesis 6–8)
    - Ark of the Covenant (Exodus 40:35 and Luke 1:35)
    - Battle of Jericho
    - Assumed
        - Psalm 132:7-8
        - Jeremiah
        - DNA

- The woman (Genesis 3; John 2:4)
    - New Eve
    - Mediatrix

- The Sign (Revelation 12)

- Mother (Revelation 12:17)

STEP 3:
SMALL-GROUP DISCUSSION

INVITATION

The Ark in the Tabernacle was the throne from which God ruled. The Old Testament Ark of the Covenant, Mary, Jesus, the Church collectively, and you and I individually all express this idea. Each is a type of ark. The kingdom of God is within you, meaning, your soul was created to be the throne of God, the place where God rules and rests, hidden within the holy of holies of your heart.

Notes

_____

_____

_____

_____

_____

_____

_____

_____

_____

_____

_____

_____

_____

_____

_____

_____

GOD PROMPT – LOVE THE WORD™

LISTEN: "There I will meet with you, and from above the mercy seat, from between the two cherubim that are upon the ark of the testimony, I will speak with you" (Exodus 25:22).

OBSERVE: One of the functions of the Ark was that of an oracle, meaning God spoke to Moses from the cloud positioned over the mercy seat, and he spoke to the high priest through the *Urim* and *Thummim* stones. In the seclusion, silence and privacy of the inner sanctuary of the Tabernacle, God audibly instructed, guided, and related to his people. Do you expect God to speak to you regarding your circumstances and life?

Remember that the Ark contained the Word of God, a memorial pot of manna, and Aaron's living rod. In what ways should your own life reflect the contents of the Ark?

Is Jesus the ruler of your heart and life? When have you allowed Jesus to be the ruler of your heart most fully?

Spend some time prayerfully reviewing your life and any particular areas in which you still want to be more obedient.

VERBALIZE: Lord, the most meaningful statement or passage of Scripture through which you spoke to me in this chapter was …

I believe that in response to my reading in this chapter, you want me to …

The thing that is the hardest about trying to hear you speak directly to me is …

 ENTRUST: *Hail Mary, full of grace, the Lord is with thee. Blessed art thou among women, and blessed is the fruit of thy womb, Jesus. Holy Mary, Mother of God, pray for us sinners, now and at the hour of our death. Amen.*

At Home in the Tabernacle

Lord, prepare me, to be a sanctuary, pure and holy, tried and true.
With thanksgiving, I'll be a living sanctuary for you. [11]

[11] Lyrics from "Sanctuary" by John W. Thompson and Randy Scruggs.

STEP 1: HOME PREPARATION

Throughout your exploration of the biblical foundations of Catholicism in the Old Testament Tabernacle, God has been calling you to dwell with him more intimately. You have been building up your very own spiritual tabernacle through your weeks of study. Whether or not you realized it, the Master Architect has been leading you as you placed one "stone" after another through our work together, so that you can share it all with others. Let us review all the ways God made the Old Testament Tabernacle worship structure new in Christ.

Maybe it seems simplistic, but "repetition is the mother of learning," they say. So by way of review, match each Old Testament element listed with its corresponding New Testament element.

Old Testament	New Testament
1. Ark	Eucharist
2. laver	high altar
3. Table of Presence Bread	Mary
4. Tabernacle	purgatory
5. Aaronite priesthood	baptismal font
6. bronze altar	prayer
7. veil	Catholic priesthood
8. solemn festivals	holy days
9. altar fire	Word of God
10. lampstand	flesh
11. incense	Church

KEY SCRIPTURE

" And I heard a loud voice from the throne saying, 'Behold, the dwelling of God is with men. He will dwell with them, and they shall be his people, and God himself will be with them. "

— **Revelation 21:3**

12 You should also be able to label each facility included in the Tabernacle compound:

13 It will take some time, but using the outline provided, see if you can indicate how each of these Old Testament types in the book of Exodus was fulfilled and is now new in the Church. The first has been done for you. If you need help, consult the responses in the back of this workbook, or discuss them in your group meeting.

Exodus 1 – God's people have become enslaved to Egypt under Pharaoh	**Romans 3:23 –** God's people are enslaved to sin
Exodus 2 – Moses is called	**Hebrews 3:5 –**
Exodus 4–6 – Moses appears before hardened Pharaoh	**1 Peter 5:8 –**
Exodus 7–11 – The ten plagues	**Romans 5:3-5 –**
Exodus 12 – Passover instituted	**Luke 22:17 – 20 –**
Exodus 12 – The Exodus	**Luke 9:29-30 –**
Exodus 13 – Firstborn consecrated	**John 3:16 –**
Exodus 14 – Delivered through the Red Sea	**1 Corinthians 10:2 and 1 Peter 3:21 –**
Exodus 16 – Manna falls	**John 6:57-58 –**
Exodus 17 – Water from the Rock	**John 4:10 –**
Exodus 18 – Moses gets leadership help	**Hebrews 13:17 –**
Exodus 19 – The people worship at Sinai	**John 4:21-24 –**
Exodus 20–23 – Moses receives the Law	**Matthew 5 –**
Exodus 24 – Israel affirms the covenant with a sacrifice and covenant meal	**1 Corinthians 11:23-30 –**
Exodus 25–31 – Instructions for the Tabernacle of worship	**1 Peter 2:5 –**
Exodus 32 – The golden calf	**Romans 7:15-25 –**
Exodus 33–34 – The covenant renewed	**Romans 8:1-2 and 1 John 1:9 –**
Exodus 35 – The people give their offerings	**Romans 12:1 and Colossians 3:22 –**
Exodus 36–40 – Building the Tabernacle	**1 Corinthians 3:9-16 –**
Exodus 40 – The cloud and the glory	**Revelation 21:2-5 –**

Isn't it amazing how carefully and deliberately God revealed his prescription and desire for proper worship through an earthly house, the Tabernacle? His preservation of the typology throughout the millennia is truly miraculous.

Aren't you overwhelmed with gratitude that Jesus, the heavenly Tabernacle, would leave heaven and run to the Cross on our behalf, fulfilling every "iota" (Matthew 5:18) of those stipulations, and then send his fulfillment forward in the Church so your heart could be his home, too?

Aren't you impressed by how diligently the Church has protected and preserved the Deposit of Faith? We are *fulfilled* in the Holy Spirit breathing through the Body of Christ, on a restless, yearning earth. God meets with us in the Church, in our own souls, in the Catholic tabernacle. He speaks to us personally. Incredible.

What joy fills my heart at the prospect that you might better understand your Catholic heritage and be more equipped to share it with others after engaging in *Fulfilled.* I thank you from the seat of my soul for the privilege. Thanks be to God.

LET'S REVIEW

The Catholic Church is the only place the whole-life worship prescribed by God in Scripture is available because:

- God is always calling us to worship in his presence.

- God explains how to worship properly.

- God asks us to make a home for him.

- I am a tabernacle of God.

- Purity in worship makes him feel "at home," and draws me into the closest possible relationship to God.

- Through the Tabernacle, God instructed that proper worship should include certain elements.

- The Old Testament Tabernacle was a copy of the sanctuary in heaven and the prototype of the Church to come.

- The Old Testament Tabernacle was the blueprint and foundation upon which Church worship and practice would be built.

- Jesus fulfills the Old Testament Tabernacle and all its elements.

- God lives in and is present to the world through the Tabernacle of the Church.

- For two-thousand years, Catholic Liturgy and worship, through Jesus—the true and final Tabernacle—has included a liturgical schedule; an institutional priesthood; a real altar; true sacrifice; purifying fire; baptismal waters; magisterial light; Eucharistic Presence Bread; fragrant prayer; guardianship of the veil; and the ark of the New Covenant.

- Through Christ, every type in the Old Testament Tabernacle has been brought forward as true antitype, alive and fully invested with saving grace, *fulfilled* in the Catholic Church.

YOU ARE NOW READY FOR THE **SESSION SEVEN VIDEO**.

STEP 2:
VIDEO PRESENTATION

Session Seven: At Home in the Tabernacle

- Unity and division

- Split in heaven and split in church

- Job 1

- Church and the fullness of truth

- Tabernacle as model for new apologetic

- New Covenant and New Ark

- Unity is mark of the Church

- Tabernacle as mini-cosmos, new heavens, and new earth

STEP 3:
SMALL-GROUP DISCUSSION

INVITATION

"Now you are the body of Christ and individually members of it" (1 Corinthians 12:27). Everything that Jesus fulfilled on earth and continues in the heavenly temple is brought forward in time through his body, the Church. In order to dwell in the closest possible relationship to God and truly be the body of Christ on earth, the Church must include all of the elements of the Old Testament Tabernacle, the messianic temple prophecies, and the heavenly worship we see in the Bible.

"Christ is the true temple of God, 'the place where his glory dwells'; by the grace of God, Christians also become the temples of the Holy Spirit, living stones out of which the Church is built" (CCC 1197).

The Catholic Church is the only Church on earth that has retained every element. Catholic faith and worship is true, heavenly worship.

Notes

_____

_____

_____

_____

_____

_____

_____

_____

_____

_____

_____

_____

_____

GOD PROMPT – LOVE THE WORD™

LISTEN: "Then he said to me, 'Prophesy to the breath, prophesy, son of man, and say to the breath, Thus says the Lord GOD: Come from the four winds, O breath, and breathe upon these slain, that they may live.' So I prophesied as he commanded me, and the breath came into them, and they lived, and stood upon their feet, an exceedingly great host" (Ezekiel 37:9-10).

OBSERVE: How has this study enriched your worship experience at Mass and in personal prayer?

Are you more convinced of the biblical reasons the Catholic Church worships and practices the way it does?

Do you feel more confident in your ability to share the biblical roots of Catholic faith with those you know and love?

How is each of the elements of the Tabernacle active in your own life?

In what area of your life do you need to feel God's presence more strongly?

VERBALIZE: Lord, after this study, I feel your presence more deeply here ...

But I still have questions about ...

Lord, I need to know that you love me unconditionally, even though the tabernacle of my body and heart is not always pure enough to welcome you ...

Now that I know my Church better, I promise to ...

ENTRUST: *Hail, Holy Queen, Mother of mercy, our life, our sweetness, and our hope. To thee do we cry, poor banished children of Eve; to thee do we send up our sighs, mourning and weeping in this valley of tears. Turn, then, most gracious advocate, thine eyes of mercy toward us, and after this, our exile, show unto us the blessed fruit of thy womb, Jesus. O clement, O loving, O sweet Virgin Mary.*

Responses

Note – Session One: Introduction has no answer key.

SESSION TWO RESPONSES: THE LIGHT OF TRUTH

1 The lampstand was to the left of the sanctuary.

2 The "one gold piece" showed unity.

3 John 15:5 shows we need unity with the "central stem," Jesus.

4 The Tabernacle menorah was decorated with almond flowers like an almond tree.

5 The almond branch symbolizes the priesthood.

6 Jesus is the High Priest at the center of the light-bearing, institutional priesthood throughout all of history.

7 Only pure oil may be used, and it must be "beaten" olive oil. The lamp must burn continuously.

8 In the pocket were the Urim and Thummim.

9 **These verses show the Urim and Thummim were used for the determination of God's will:**

Numbers 27:21	–	used to consult God on selection of leaders
1 Samuel 14:41	–	used for determination of guilt
Ezra 2:63	–	used for determination of God's will concerning captives

10 Sirach 45:10 calls the Urim and Thummim "the oracle of judgment."

11 **The main association the Jews had with light is shown in these verses:**

Genesis 1:1-5	–	light of creation
Exodus 10:21-23	–	salvation from Egyptian plague of darkness
Exodus 13:17-22	–	pillar of fire

Psalm 27:1   –   "the LORD is my light and my salvation," or "saving light"
Isaiah 60:19   –   "the LORD will be your everlasting light"
Job 29:3   –   light in the darkness
Micah 7:8   –   "the LORD will be a light to me"

12 The verses above illustrate that light was a metaphor in Old Testament Judaism for the presence of God.

13 Jesus says, "I am the light of the world" (John 8:12).

14 Jesus means he is a spiritual light.

15 The Feast of Tabernacles was a remembrance of God's provision in the wilderness and his guidance through Moses, the Law, and the cloud.

16 These four lampstands symbolized God's presence in the Temple.

17 The leaders knew him to be claiming equality with God.

18 Oral traditions and written traditions make up authentic apostolic teaching.

19 No, the Bible cannot be a Christian's only authority.

20 **These passages speak about the interpretation of Scripture:**

2 Peter 1:20   –   No prophecy of Scripture is a matter of private interpretation
Revelation 19:10 –   All prophecy is Jesus
John 5:39-40   –   All Scripture is prophecy/Jesus

21 These passages show that none of Scripture is a matter of private interpretation.

22 We find authoritative, reliable interpretation in the Church.

SESSION THREE RESPONSES: THE BREAD OF LIFE

1. Melchizedek was a priest and king of "Salem." Personal responses may vary.

2. This great event in Israelite history was the Passover.

3. Passover was important because it was the Israelites' redemption.

4. Bread was part of the annual commemoration.

5. No leaven was eaten for seven days, showing the covenant, and there was no leaven in the Passover bread.

6. The Israelites were in a hurry.

7. This is an annual sign of the covenant with the Lord and their redemption in him.

8. Manna was bread or food from heaven.

9. It appeared with the dew.

10. It looked and tasted like honey cakes.

11. The people could use it baked, boiled, ground, or raw.

12. Manna appeared for forty years.

13. Manna was complete nutrition.

14. The people could only gather a one-day supply of manna, except before the Sabbath. Then they could gather a two-day supply.

15. These instructions were to teach them that God will always provide daily bread.

16. His sustenance was conformed to every taste.

17   This meal (verse 11) foreshadowed the Eucharist. Personal responses will vary.

18   This table was used for the Presence Bread.

19   There were twelve loaves laid out with frankincense, which was offered with fire. The bread was a perpetual offering, and priests cared for it on the Sabbath.

20   The loaves represented the twelve tribes and foreshadowed the twelve apostles.

21   It was integral because it showed nourishment is from God.

22   This observance was to last forever.

23   Hebrews 5:5-6 speaks of Melchizedek.

24   Luke 9:28-36 records the Transfiguration.

25   Moses, Elijah, and Jesus spoke about Jesus' exodus or "departure."

26   There will be a new exodus.

27   **John 6 – headings:**

Feeding the five thousand
Jesus walks on water
Bread from heaven
Words of eternal life
Rejected by his own
Many disciples turn away

28   Jesus says, "I am the bread of life" (John 6:35).

29   He means that he is eternal life.

30   Many turned away.

31 ▸ This prayer is the Our Father.

32 ▸ Responses will vary.

33 ▸ Responses will vary.

34 ▸ Responses will vary.

35 ▸ St. Paul teaches that the Eucharist is a participation that unifies.

36 ▸ Not "discerning" his body is to be guilty of it.

SESSION FOUR RESPONSES: HOLY SMOKE

1 ▸ The incense altar was made of gold.

2 ▸ It was positioned directly in front of the Holy of Holies.

3 ▸ The gold shows that incense is "divine"—it originates from God and ascends to God.

4 ▸ Horns symbolize spiritual authority and power.

5 ▸ Once a year, the horns were anointed with the blood of atonement, so that the incense was "cleansed" of sin.

6 ▸ Incense was burned morning and evening.

7 ▸ The incense ritual was never to cease.

8 ▸ Luke 1:10 refers to the "hour of incense." Personal responses may vary.

9 ▸ It was the perfumer's responsibility to make the incense and oil.

10 ▸ Responses will vary.

11 ▸ Responses will vary.

12 · Frankincense was used as a gift to the baby Jesus.

13 · Incense stands for prayer.

14 · Jesus called the Cross and Passion his "hour."

15 · This was Jesus' prayer before the Lord at his "hour of incense." Personal responses may vary.

16 · Responses will vary.

17 · Responses will vary.

18 · This reference is to Psalm 22:1. In the RSV-CE, the reference is indicated by an asterisk and is located at the bottom of the page or in the Explanatory Notes at the end of the New Testament in Appendix 1.

19 · Jesus applies Psalm 22 to himself.

20 · This reference is to Psalm 31:5. In the RSV-CE, the reference is indicated by an asterisk and is located at the bottom of the page or in the Explanatory Notes at the end of the New Testament in Appendix 1.

21 · Jesus quotes the Psalms at his "hour."

22 · Jesus offers his prayers as incense to God.

23 · The psalmist prayed seven times a day.

24 · Saints Peter and John were headed to the Temple "at the hour of prayer" (Acts 3:1).

25 · St. Peter had gone to the rooftop to observe noon prayers.

26 · The verses refer to Psalm 2:1-2. Comparisons will vary.

27 · The prayers of the Church are described as "golden bowls full of incense" (Revelation 5:8).

28. They are praying to the Lamb.

29. Our prayers, especially those of the martyrs, are "incense" burning in altar fire in the heavenly temple.

30. Responses will vary.

31. The heavenly incense altar is adorned with horns.

32. The "pure offering" would be accompanied by incense (Malachi 1:11).

33. In Mark 11:15-17, Jesus affirms non-Jewish and Jewish prayer in his "house."

SESSION FIVE RESPONSES: HOLY OF HOLIES

1. This tapestry was made of "fine twined linen" (Exodus 26:31).

2. It faced east, the direction of the advent of Christ.

3. Matthew 24:27 refers to the Second Coming.

4. Cherubim were woven into the curtain.

5. Angels were guarding the Garden and the way to the Tree of Life.

6. Something within the veil must have also led to the Tree of Life.

7. It was used to wrap the Ark of the Covenant for protection.

8. Blue, scarlet, and purple were used to make the veil.

9. Responses will vary.

10. *Sakak* means "knit" in this verse.

11 Jesus' body is the temple. The presence of God once screened from view in the Holy of Holies is now enfleshed and visible in Christ.

12 Jesus is the flesh and blood revelation of God.

13 Jesus was accompanied by angels at the Annunciation, at his birth, after his temptation, in Gethsemane, and at his resurrection.

14 Each of us has a guardian angel.

15 Responses will vary.

16 After Jesus quoted Psalm 22:1, the Temple veil was rent in two.

17 Hebrews 9 shows that the way to God was opened; the heavenly Holy of Holies was no longer closed.

18 The "second veil" is the flesh that prevents "sight" of God in the heavenly temple.

19 The *Catechism of the Catholic Church* explains that the Church will undergo a passion in the last days (CCC 675–677).[12]

20 The Tabernacle veil screened the presence of God on the Ark as the gate in Ezekiel 44 "screened" the entrance to the new Temple, Jesus' presence in Mary's womb.

SESSION SIX RESPONSES: THE THRONE OF GOD

1 Behind the veil was the Ark of the Covenant.

2 It was made of acacia wood.

3 The Ark was plated with gold.

---

[12] Cf. Lk 18:8; Mt 24:12.

4 ⟩ In the Bible, wood is symbolic of humanity, while gold is symbolic of divinity, so that the wood and gold of the Ark suggest humanity overlaid with holiness or divinity.

5 ⟩ The poles and rings were for easy transport.

6 ⟩ The lid of the Ark was the "mercy seat" (Exodus 25:17).

7 ⟩ Responses will vary.

8 ⟩ The high priest was to sprinkle the blood of atonement on the mercy seat seven times.

9 ⟩ Because the blood of the sacrificial victim made atonement for the people and was brought directly into his presence, the mercy seat was the place where God's justice and mercy met.

10 ⟩ The mercy seat was made of gold.

11 ⟩ Cherubim gazed perpetually down at the mercy seat.

12 ⟩ The Ark was carefully guarded and protected. It was surrounded by worship, privacy, and mystery.

13 ⟩ The word "coffin" suggests that the Ark was somehow a place of suffering and death, as is also indicated by the blood of atonement sprinkled there on the Day of Atonement.

14 ⟩ It was called the "Oracle" because God would speak from the mercy seat.

15 ⟩ The term "oracle" implies it was an audible voice, and the Church Fathers believed so.

16 ⟩ This was a literal presence. The people saw the pillar of cloud and fire. Moses spoke to God and heard him from the mercy seat. They would not have been afraid of a symbol.

17 ▸ The Ark contained the "Testimony" or Ten Commandments.

18 ▸ In the context of the Liturgy of the Word at Mass, the "Word" is Scripture and Commandment.

19 ▸ The Ark contained manna and Aaron's rod.

20 ▸ Hebrews 9:3-5 mentions a container of manna, Aaron's rod, and the Ten Commandments.

21 ▸ God sent Jesus to be "an expiation by his blood" (Romans 3:25).

22 ▸ Jesus is the new Manna because he is the Eucharist.

23 ▸ Jesus is the new Rod of Aaron because he is the High Priest.

24 ▸ Jesus is the final Covenant because he is the Word of God.

25 ▸ **Personal responses will vary.**

Genesis 1:2-3	–	The Holy Spirit is "moving over" the waters.
Exodus 40:34-35	–	The Holy Spirit "covered" the tent and "abode" on the Tabernacle.
Luke 1:35	–	The Holy Spirit will "overshadow" Mary.

26 ▸ St. John saw the ark in the heavenly tabernacle.

27 ▸ The first word is "and."

28 ▸ This woman is Mary.

SESSION SEVEN RESPONSES: AT HOME IN THE TABERNACLE

Matching Old Testament to New Testament elements:

1. Ark   Mary
2. laver   baptismal font
3. Table of Presence Bread   Eucharist
4. Tabernacle   Church
5. Aaronite priesthood   Catholic priesthood
6. bronze altar   high altar
7. veil   flesh
8. solemn festivals   holy days
9. altar fire   purgatory
10. lampstand   Word of God
11. incense   prayer

12. Labeling done directly on the workbook page.

13 **Answers to 13 listed below.**

Romans 3:23 – God's people are enslaved to sin

Hebrews 3:5 – Jesus is Son; a New Moses

1 Peter 5:8 – the devil is my enemy

Romans 5:3-5 – perseverance is required

Luke 22:17-20 – a new Passover

Luke 9:29-30 – a new exodus

John 3:16 – a true firstborn

1 Corinthians 10:2 and 1 Peter 3:21 – a new baptism

John 6:57-58 – a new manna

John 4:10 – living water

Hebrews 13:17 – a new hierarchy in Christ

John 4:21-24 – a new location for worship; Christ

Matthew 5 – a new law

1 Corinthians 11:23-30 – a New Covenant meal

1 Peter 2:5 – a new tabernacle of living stones

Romans 7:15-25 – a new idolatry

Romans 8:1-2 and 1 John 1:9 – new promise of forgiveness and renewal

Romans 12:1 and Colossians 3:22 – new works; whatever you do, do it unto the Lord

1 Corinthians 3:9-16 – building on the new foundation of Christ with our works

Revelation 21:2-5 – the dwelling place of God is with men forever; all things are new